Our Baby

written by Jay Dale
illustrated by Andrew Everitt-Stewart

Rosie looked at Mum.
Her tummy was big and round.
"When will our baby come?"
asked Rosie.

"Soon," said Mum.

3

The next day, Mum's tummy
still looked big and round.

"When will our baby come?"
asked Rosie.

"Soon," said Mum.

"Will our baby come today?" said Rosie.

"Maybe," smiled Mum.
But the baby didn't come.

The next day, Rosie put her hand
on Mum's tummy.
She rubbed her hand up and down.
Then she put her cheek on top.
"Hello, baby," she said.
But the baby didn't say a thing.

The next morning,
when Rosie woke up,
Granny was sitting on the sofa.

"Hello, Granny," said Rosie.
"Where's Mum?"

"Mum and Dad are at the hospital,"
said Granny.

"Is our baby coming?" asked Rosie.

"Yes!" said Granny.
"Our baby **is** coming."

Granny and Rosie
got into a big yellow taxi.
They went down the street
and up the hill.

"Here we are," said Granny.

"This is the hospital."

Granny and Rosie went inside.
They walked by lots of babies.

"Is this our baby?" asked Rosie.

"No," said Granny.
"That's not our baby."

"Is this our baby?" asked Rosie.

"No," said Granny.
"That's not our baby."

"Where's **our** baby?" asked Rosie.

Granny just smiled.
"Come with me," she said.

Granny and Rosie
peeped around a big door.

"Come in, Rosie," smiled Mum.
"I have missed you so much!"

Mum was sitting up in a big bed.
Her tummy was not big.
Her tummy was not round.

Then Rosie saw a little bed.

The bed was next to Dad.

She went over and peeped inside.

"Is this our baby?" asked Rosie.

"Yes!" smiled Mum.

"Yes!" smiled Dad.

"Yes!" smiled Granny.
"This is **our** baby."